MAHOGANY

STEPS TO CUTTING, COLOURING AND FINISHING HAIR

Martin Gannon
and Richard Thompson

First published 1997 by
MACMILLAN PRESS LTD
Houndmills, Basingstoke, Hampshire RG21 6XS
and London
Companies and representatives
throughout the world

ISBN 0–333–69949–1

A catalogue record for this book is available
from the British Library.

This book is printed on paper suitable for recycling and made from fully managed and sustained forest sources.

10   9   8   7   6   5   4   3   2   1
06   05   04   03   02   01   00   99   98   97

Printed in Great Britain by Jarrold Book Printing, Thetford, Norfolk.

HAIRDRESSING TRAINING BOARD/MACMILLAN SERIES

If you would like to receive future titles in the Hairdressing Training Board/Macmillan series as they are published, you can make use of our standing order facility. Contact your bookseller, quoting series standing order ISBN 0–333–69338–8 or, in the case of difficulty, write to us at the address below with your name and address, the title of the series and the ISBN quoted above.

Customer Services Department, Macmillan Distribution Ltd
Houndmills, Basingstoke, Hampshire RG21 6XS, England

NOTE ABOUT PRONOUNS

Using 'he or she' and 'him or her' throughout the text would become cumbersome in a book such as this. For simplicity and ease of reading, therefore, we have generally used 'she' and 'her' except in passages concerned specifically with men's hairdressing.

CONTENTS

MARTIN GANNON
Co-Founder and Managing Director

Over twenty years ago, Martin Gannon joined forces with Richard Thompson to found the now well-known Mahogany group of salons. With a clear picture of the creative and business profile of the company, Martin is responsible for co-ordinating Mahogany's UK and international activities.

RICHARD THOMPSON
Co-Founder and International Creative Director

The name of Richard Thompson and that of Mahogany are almost synonymous, such is his contribution to the inspiring and technically precise atmosphere that the group represents. Consistently working within the original philosophy to be on the cutting edge, Richard provides the general artistic direction of the company and is responsible for developing and presenting Mahogany's international creative image.

RUSSELL BARKER
Commercial Director

Russell has played an integral role in the commercial success of Mahogany since its inception. After ten years as part of the creative directorship of Mahogany, Russell began to concentrate on the commercial aspects of the business. He is primarily responsible for managing over a hundred Mahogany staff, the export of Mahogany's range of trade products and the general financial management of the company.

COLIN GREANEY
UK Creative Director

Colin began his training at Mahogany in 1981. Quickly establishing a reputation for creative innovation, Colin was promoted to Artistic Director in 1985, UK Creative Director in 1989 and became a company director in 1992. Working closely with Richard Thompson, Colin has travelled the world promoting and representing the Mahogany ethos. He now heads the Mahogany flagship salon in Mayfair.

ANTONY LICATA

Salons Creative Director

Antony started working in the Mahogany Oxford salon in 1984. By 1987 he was promoted to manage the busy Turl Street salon and he became a director of the company in 1992. Since 1995, Antony has been responsible for the training direction of all the Mahogany salons. He divides his time between the five salons and the Mahogany Training Academy, ensuring that a clear artistic direction is adhered to throughout the company.

MARK CREED

Head of Technical Development

Mark started his career at Mahogany in 1984. He soon realised that his main interest lay in the artistic possibilities in the application of colour and perm. Based at the Turl Street salon, Mark was soon promoted to Head of Technical Development. He travels internationally, demonstrating his skills, and is responsible for developing new trade products and techniques. Mark is responsible for the internal training of Mahogany staff.

KARL FORSYTH-GRAY

Technical Director for the London Salon

Karl began working in the Mahogany flagship London salon in 1995. With an interesting career spanning the Royal Shakespeare Company and hairdressing training in Japan and Germany, Karl is now a specialist in colouring and perming, leading the technical development of the Mayfair salon and attending to many celebrity clients.

Salons at:

17 ST GEORGE STREET, HANOVER SQUARE
LONDON W1R 9DE
TELEPHONE 0171 629 3121

5 TURL STREET
OXFORD OX1 3DQ
TELEPHONE 01865 248143

30 LITTLE CLARENDON STREET
OXFORD OX1 2HU
TELEPHONE 01865 552494

5 MARKET STREET
OXFORD OX1 3EF
TELEPHONE 01865 790245

1 NEW BOND STREET PLACE
BATH BA1 1EA
TELEPHONE 01225 466967

CENTRAL OFFICE: 5 TURL STREET
OXFORD OX1 3DQ
TELEPHONE 01865 791332
FAX 01865 722454

PREFACE

From the conception of the original Mahogany salon in 1979, Martin Gannon and Richard Thompson knew they had a very special creative energy. Together they forged out highly polished hairdressing techniques, founding a base on which to build a unique and recognisable style. Mahogany has developed a training programme which has enabled the original team of five to grow into a hairdressing group famous world-wide, with five successful salons, a hundred staff and a flagship situated in Mayfair, the fashion centre of London.

This their first book has attempted, we hope successfully, to illustrate in step-by-step detail the Mahogany approach to cutting, colouring and finishing modern hair. It explains clearly the most important elements in a professional hairdressing service.

When Martin Gannon and Richard Thompson first established Mahogany, fashion was a word people cared about and responded to. Now fashion is about individuality and personal need rather than the imposition of a particular image on the client. The fashion mood is constantly changing and new fashion directions are being influenced by the people. Therefore, hairdressers and the hairdressing industry must always be changing to satisfy that need.

This book portrays the Mahogany view of the new classics – cutting and colouring techniques that can be expanded to produce more avant-garde styles or used in commercial work on your clients.

We hope you enjoy Mahogany's techniques for cutting, colouring and finishing.

Unless otherwise stated, cuts are by Richard Thompson of Mahogany.

PART 1: BACKGROUND

How we approach day-to-day activities
within the salon structure.

SALON AMBIENCE

The ambience of a salon should be energetic and at the same time relaxing for the client. In order to create the right environment for both staff and clients, the following points should be considered.

RECEPTION

The moment a client walks through your door she senses the ambience of the salon – the efficiency, the welcome, the images of the people working there, all these impressions are soon noted and subconsciously stored.

The reception may include a retail area offering a wide range of professional hair care products which will support and maintain clients' hair between salon visits. It should be attractive and uncluttered.

IMAGES COLOUR LIBRARY

IMAGES COLOUR LIBRARY

B & O LOUDSPEAKERS LTD

DECOR

The decoration of a salon is a matter of the owner's personal taste. However, the overall success of the salon's appearance will also be determined by an awareness of the clientele you want to attract, of what is acceptable to a variety of people and of what is fashionable in interior design.

MUSIC

Music is also very personal, but in a hairdressing salon where communication between stylist and client is of paramount importance, music should be interesting without being dominant. What type of music would suit your clientele? Will the music you choose help to create a relaxing or a stimulating environment?

Keep the speakers away from reception and position them high up so that no one has to sit in a direct blast of sound.

AIR CONDITIONING

Air conditioning removes negative ions, keeping the air fresh and clean and free from unpleasant chemical odour and cigarette smoke (if you allow smoking in the salon). It will also cool or heat the space.

GOWNS AND TOWELS

Gowns should feel very comfortable, be protective and fit all shapes and sizes. The best are made of a silky drip-dry fabric. You should be able to have the neck of a gown tight or loose to facilitate cutting different lengths of hair. Towels should be thickish and soft and large enough to form a turban on the head – an attractive and secure option to finish and present a client in preparation for styling, colouring or perming, and a more glamorous image for the client. The comfort factor creates an attitude, the attitude creates an overall ambience.

REFRESHMENTS

Teas, coffees, mineral water, juice – which should you offer? We find that increasingly people are asking for herbal tea, decaffeinated coffee and tea. We believe it is best to provide a varied but concise selection, served in cups that are easy to stack, easy to carry and easy to hold.

PHILOSOPHY

WHAT IS THE MAHOGANY PHILOSOPHY AND WHY DO WE HAVE ONE?

It's probably more of a formula – the procedures we follow,
everything we can possibly do to keep a loyal clientele.

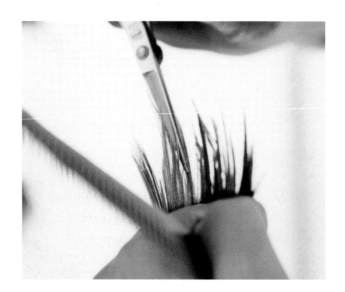

CUTTING

All Mahogany staff are trained within a system which consists of
three-month modules over a two-year period. Each module covers a
different aspect. Consistency of quality and procedure creates a
confident, loyal clientele.

Let's take an example. Stylist Tom always cuts Miss Smith's hair, but
Tom is away and Susie cuts it instead. Because all Mahogany stylists
use just one pair of scissors to create a look and because they have all
been trained within the same system, Miss Smith's hair will be cut
using the same tools, and the same procedure. The client will feel that
there is a consistency in procedure and technique and is more likely to
be a happy client.

Now let's take another example. All the stylists in the salon use
different tools for cutting hair – Tom uses scissors and a razor, Susie
uses scissors and thinning scissors. Tom is away and Miss Smith, Tom's
loyal client, goes to Susie. Instead of using a razor, Suzie uses thinning
scissors. Immediately the client will feel unsure and will more than
likely question this procedure. This will take away the confidence of
both the client and the stylist. When Tom returns to work he is likely
to have lost the client, or the client will complain to him about how
the cut wasn't the same.

It is Mahogany's theory that under these circumstances a business
cannot grow, because the client comes to depend on an individual
stylist's experience not on the experience of the whole salon.

A salon's experience represents business growth. It is not necessarily our philosophy that using razors or thinning scissors is bad, but we do believe that whatever you decide to use as a team, you should all use it in the same way and with consistency for the looks and fashion at a particular time. If a client feels secure and can trust the salon, she will be loyal. This in turn has great value for each and every stylist working within that salon.

This same philosophy applies to colouring, shampooing and drying procedures. Whatever tools you use and whatever procedures and techniques you follow, there has to be salon consistency.

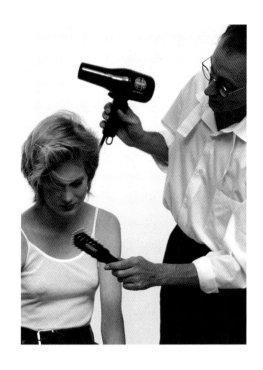

CHANGE

For a client a change might simply be the way you dry the hair or the positioning of the parting. For a hairdresser, however, a change generally consists in cutting the hair or changing the colour. Sometimes a subtle change is all that's needed to modernise a particular look. Sometimes the client is looking for a more radical approach.

How do we establish what sort of change is change?

Pictures! Pictures or magazine images can help the stylist understand what the client likes. These should not be copied exactly, as if the style were written in stone, but they can be used to establish a lead or direction towards the client's aesthetics and lifestyle. They can help you understand how a client perceives herself or how she would like to be perceived. These images give you a starting point to be able to discuss what the right look for your client might be. You can then take into account the hair type, density, growth patterns and face shape to personalise the chosen images to that particular client.

IMAGE BANK

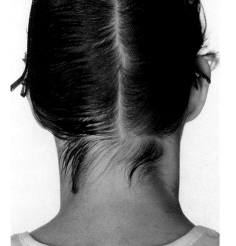

CLIENT CONSULTATION

Approach

When you approach a client for the first time you are subconsciously taking account of the way she looks, the way she is dressed, her mannerisms, skin tone and hair type. You are almost deciding what you feel is going to be the best look for the client and what is possible with her hair type. Meanwhile, the client is doing exactly the same thing about you as her stylist, the atmosphere and cleanliness of the salon, the gowns, etc. Therefore, your approach to the start of the conversation and your body language are all important.

For example, if you walk up to a client, rest your scissors and comb on her shoulder with one hand, finger her hair with the other, and say hello, you are likely to arouse apprehension. However, if you put down your comb and scissors, face the client as you introduce yourself, then go on to talk hair, you will get a much more open response.

When you talk about the client's hair, try to find out what she doesn't like about it. This will tell you what she is looking for and immediately puts you in a better position to advise her.

For example, during the consultation the client might have told you about a previous colour or cut or about the condition – that she didn't like the shade, that the hair was too heavy, the cut too short, etc. This opens the way for you to discuss all the services the salon has to offer. (You may wish to involve a colouring technician in the discussion of the benefits of colouring.) If, on the other hand, you just ask 'What can I do for you today?', the client will probably reply in one of two ways: 'You're the professional, what do you think?' or 'I would like this much cut off'. Both these replies give you no information at all about your client.

Once you get into this position you might have to ask 'What did you have in mind?' This leaves the client in control and nine times out of ten she will not get what she would really like because she probably won't know what that is until you suggest it to her. However, if you can find out what the client doesn't want, you are at the start of a more creative route.

Key factors in client–hairdresser communication

1 Give the client time to explain her needs and listen to what she says. Remember that she has had many experiences – both positive and negative – from previous hairstyling services.

2 Always offer clear, honest and, above all, sensitive advice. Never use too much technical or professional jargon. This will only confuse the client's expectations and make her feel insecure.

3 The hairdresser's priorities in communicating with the client should be:

• Offer two or three style options to suit hair type, hair growth pattern and the client's lifestyle and personal look.

• Offer and recommend the best hair products for preparation and aftercare. Concentrate on the essential products that will enable clients to manage their hair after leaving the salon. Healthy-hair clients are happy clients.

• When you are cutting your client's hair for the first time, always ask her to assess how she manages her hair between salon visits. Such information could be crucial to your advice and choice of recommended style – the more emphasis on the haircut controlling the shape, the better. This priority will make your client's life hassle-free, and she will thank you for that.

• Finally, when your client is preparing to leave the salon, advise her when it would be appropriate to return for the next appointment. And remember to wish your client farewell! Most clients appreciate this personal touch, and attention to detail is all important.

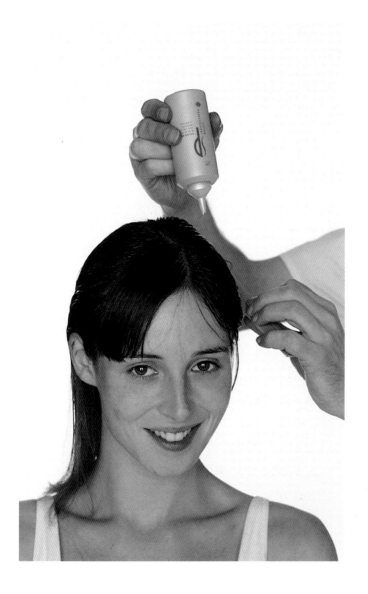

COLOURING

WHAT IS COLOUR?

When we observe hair colour what we in fact see is reflected light.

Natural white light is made up of a combination of seven colours: red, orange, yellow, green, blue, indigo and violet. These seven colours as pigments in the hair shaft – on their own or in combination – reflect or absorb light and allow us to perceive the hair colour.

The three primary colours are red, yellow and blue. Combining these colours gives you three secondary tones:

red + yellow = orange

yellow + blue = green

blue + red = purple

When colouring hair it is important to work in as near white-light (i.e. daylight) conditions as possible, so that you can perceive true colours. Many artificial lights lack some of the colours present in white light.

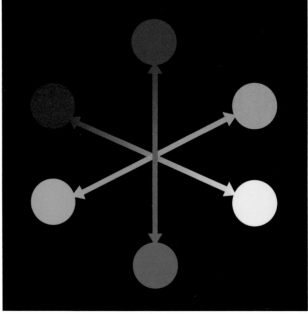

COLOUR

Hair colour is divided into depth and tone. Depth, also called base colour, indicates how light or dark the hair is, e.g. blonde or brown. Tone is the visual reflective quality of the colour, e.g. red or gold or ash.

In natural hair, two types of pigment are present: ashen pigments and warm pigments. The elongated molecules of ashen pigments appear as black or brown and are the easiest to remove when lightening the hair. The warm pigments are red and yellow. These molecules are more difficult to remove as they are smaller and spherical and are fused better into the hair structure.

Make-up: Honey Twiggs   Clothes styling: Cheryl Konteh   Photo: Grey Zisser

PERMANENT COLOUR

Permanent colours, also known as para dyes, work by mimicking natural pigments and in some cases by masking them. They work by chemical reaction between the dye substance and hydrogen peroxide.

The dye contains the colouring agent and ammonia, also such additions as conditioning polymers, in an emulsion base. The ammonia has two functions. Firstly, it opens up the cuticle of the hair shaft to allow the colouring agent to enter the hair. Secondly, it activates the hydrogen peroxide, as hydrogen peroxide will only give up its oxygen in an alkaline state.

Once in the hair shaft, the free oxygen molecules join the colourless colouring molecules and they swell and the colour develops. Once swollen they become insoluble in water and too large to rinse from a normal hair shaft.

TEMPORARY
COLOURS

These types of colour come in
many forms. Most are applied to
wet hair and they coat the hair's
surface. The colour pigments are
positively charged and are
attracted to the negatively charged
hair. The pigments are very often
vegetable-based.

TIPS

● Temporary colours cannot
change the base colour of the
hair and will wash out of
normal hair in 1 to 6
shampoos. They can be used
to top up fading permanent
colour between tints.

● Colour may be applied to
the hair straight from an
applicator bottle, but a tint
bowl and brush is the
preferred method because it
looks more professional.

PHOTO: GREY ZISSER

BLEACHING PRODUCTS

Bleach is basically an alkalising agent which, when added to hydrogen peroxide, releases the oxygen in the peroxide into the hair shaft. This breaks down the hair's natural pigmentation.

It comes in two basic forms – a powder or an oil emulsion. Powder bleach is the stronger of the two and is used widely for off-scalp processes such as highlighting. Adjusting the peroxide strength will alter the lifting ability of the bleach.

Oil emulsion works in the same way but it is a gentler lightening agent used for on-scalp application. The strength is adjusted by the addition of boosters.

Bleaches contain ammonia, ammonium hydroxide, ammonium persulfate silicates and sodium.

TIPS

● When you are bleaching regrowth, never re-apply bleach to other areas of the hair – there should be no overlap. Bleaching is a very strong chemical process and must be carried out with great care.

● Even a strong bleach may not remove all the yellow pigment and a toner may be used to cover this yellow.

● If you lift bleach to white it will not hold a toner.

TIPS

● Remember that the name tone on tone indicates that these colours add pigment to the hair and therefore you must be careful when choosing the right colour. Less than 50% grey, you should use a lighter base colour than the client's. For example, if the client's base colour is light brown, do not apply light brown – the result would be dark brown, as you have added pigment to the hair.

● It is common practice at Mahogany to colour a client's hair before the cut if the cut isn't going to be a total change, i.e. from long to short.

TONE ON TONE COLOURS

Tone on tone colours have largely replaced the older type of semi-permanent colours, which are now known as temporary colours. This is because of the modern habit of shampooing every day, which removes the old colour too quickly.

Unlike the older semis, tone on tone semis enter into the hair shaft to a greater degree, and produce stronger and longer-lasting colours.

They are mixed with a colour developer which contains hydrogen peroxide at between 2% and 4% and are applied to wet hair following a shampoo with a detoxifying cleanser.

Why as hairdressers do we want to produce a photograph of a hairstyle?

There are a variety of reasons: you may wish to use the image to promote cutting or dressing techniques to your salon clients, or to promote a colour or styling product. Or you may want to use it to promote your own hairdressing skill to the trade. Whatever the reason, the way you are going to use the image should help determine your choice of model and hair type. You should also bear in mind where the image is likely to appear, e.g. in a magazine or newspaper, on a poster, promotional leaflet or salon price list.

BOOKING A PHOTO SESSION

The following points should be considered:

1 Type of model
2 Style of photographs
3 Style of make-up
4 Choice of studio
5 Clothes image
6 Type of film
7 Head and shoulders or three-quarter length?
8 Planning ahead
9 Lunches for the team

Let us explore each of the above points.

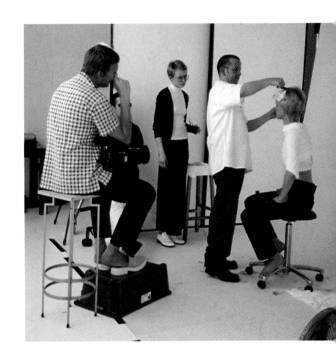

PHOTO: MAUREEN BARRYMORE

1 Type of model

How you intend to use the photographs will determine your choice of model. Some models have a more commercially viable face, whereas others are stronger and will make more of a statement but they will not necessarily sell magazines. The colour of the hair and eyes will also have an influence on this. For example, in certain countries red hair is seen as evil, therefore if you choose a red-haired model you will have little hope of getting your image published in those countries. On the other hand, in some other countries red hair will guarantee you a cover. So make sure your choice of model is appropriate for what you hope to achieve.

2 Style of photographs

Different photographers have different styles and different expertise.
To produce good hair shots you need a cross between a beauty photographer
and a fashion photographer. Check out their books and meet them in person
so that you can discuss the shots in their books that you like. You may prefer
a compilation of a few shots. If so, ask whether this is possible, explore the
options.

3 Style of make-up

Photographers usually have their favourite make-up artists that understand
their lighting techniques and the tone achieved on the film they use. Meet the
make-up artist and discuss the possibilities, showing him or her your choice of
model. Remember, skin tone can change the entire make-up image you may
have been planning.

4 Choice of studio

Generally there are two types: daylight studios where you may
use less artificial light and rely on natural light, or blackout
studios where you use only artificial light. The image you are
looking for and the style of photographs will determine which
type of studio you choose. A location shoot is another option,
but it is rife with problems. For instance, a beach shoot would
make a fabulous day out but if it's blowing a gale and/or
raining you may end up in a cave with a flashlight. Hair is the
important thing. Location shoots are better suited to fashion
photography.

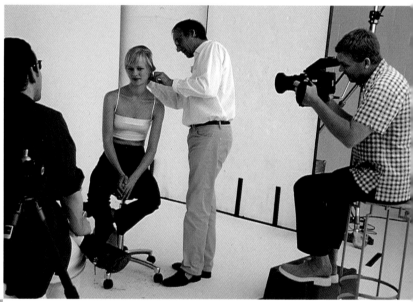

5 Clothes image

Clean and simple necklines do not detract from a hairstyle if you are
going just for head and shoulders. If you want a three-quarter look,
you will need to get hold of different outfits.

You may decide to employ a clothes stylist. If so, see their books and
talk to them. A good result from a photo shoot depends on the
whole team.

6 Type of film

There are three basic types of colour film: transparency, negative and polaroid.

Transparency This type gives you finished transparencies in various sizes – 35 mm, $2\frac{1}{4}$ " or 6″ x 4″. Basically, the larger the transparency the sharper the look. 35 mm is the cheapest. 6 x 4 is the most expensive. $2\frac{1}{4}$ is a good balance for hair shots. Subsequent touch-ups can be expensive as they have to be digitally remastered.

Negative Negative film comes in the same sizes as transparency and you receive colour contact sheets to view. Although this is a more expensive process overall, you have better control. Touch-ups can be done by hand off a print and then the original print re-shot as many times as you like.

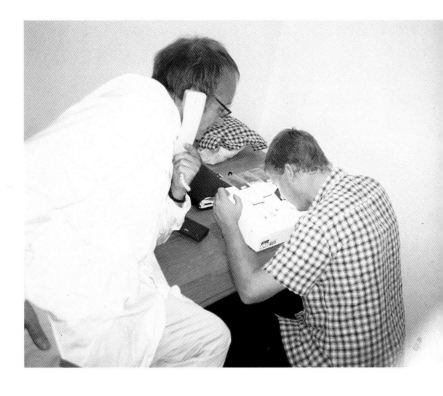

Polaroid Polaroids are indispensable for seeing if your look is coming together before you go to film. This type of Polaroid is never used as a finished look but as a test shot. There is also another type of Polaroid which is used for a finished look – the large-format 10″ x 8″. Although each shot is expensive, seeing the finished print in minutes is a great advantage and you can stop when you have your ultimate shot. This photograph can then be re-shot onto a transparency film. We have used this process many times with tremendous success.

7 Head and shoulders or three-quarter length?

A magazine cover is generally a head-and-shoulders shot. Inside, as an editorial, the shot can be longer. So you might use one of the models for a cover shot but then shoot her three-quarter length in case the cover shot is unsuitable.

8 Planning ahead

A photo session can be one of the most rewarding experiences but only if it is well organised and thought through completely.

Do not try to do more than three models a day and go for two finished looks on each one. Have the images in your head before you start and an organised plan of the order of your shots. If you have two blondes and one dark model, do all the blonde shots together rather than putting the dark shots in the middle, otherwise the lighting will have to be altered and this process wastes time. Think ahead so that you have no dead spots during the day. Time is money – and a photo session eats both!

9 Lunches for the team

A photo session can be a long day and it is a team effort. A stop for a good buffet-style lunch works for everybody – a happy team will produce results! You may have as many as 10–12 people on the day so make sure you budget for this.

Good hair shots are always needed by the trade and consumer magazines – have fun with it and the shots will be fabulous.

PART 2: TECHNIQUES

The basics to start from.

ONE LENGTH BOB

Precision-cut outline without graduation.

Cutting

The model's hair was very grown out from her previous haircut and was looking lack-lustre, with remnants of 'Sun-In' on the ends.

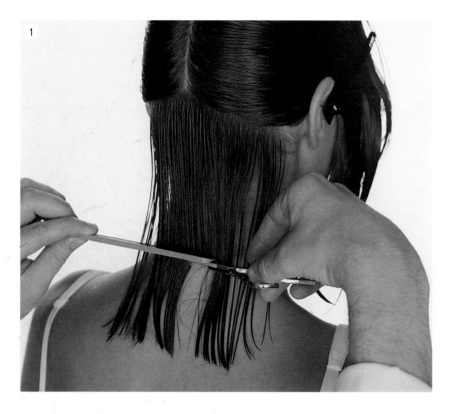

1

Take your first panel horizontally on the occipital bone from the centre back to behind the ears. Comb hair thoroughly. Use the comb to hold the hair at the desired length, then cut. Start from the centre and create a gentle convex curve. The head must be tilted very slightly forward.

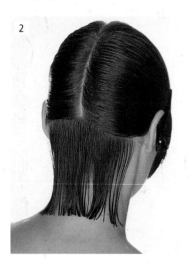

2

3

4

Once you have completed your guide line, continue taking sections in this fashion. Each section should be approximately 2 cm wide. As you work up above the occipital bone your sections should become diagonal and should not go above the top of the ears. Stop when you reach the crown.

5

6

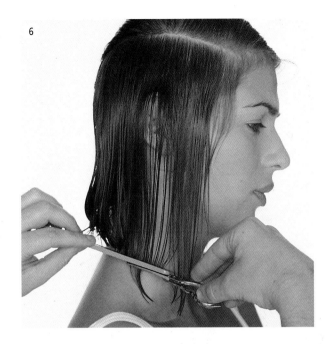

7

Your next panel should be the side. Take the horizontal section (at least 2 cm wide) above the ear. Comb hair thoroughly and gently press the back of your scissors on to the hair above the ear. Hold your scissors here until your comb reaches the desired length (i.e. following on from the guide line you cut in step 4) and cut. The head should be upright but very slightly tilted away from you. Work up to the centre top in this way, then do the same on the other side.

TIP

Pressing your scissors on to the hair above the ear allows for any disruption of the base line by the hair which is falling over the ear.

Colouring

1

Take a section 4 cm from the front of the hairline and place a fine woven section on top of a Colour Wrap. Apply the tint using a Colour Stroker.

2

3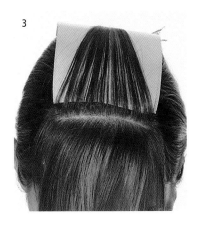

Fold the Colour Wrap to create a sealed packet. Then leave a fine mesh uncoloured. Continue this working pattern to the front hairline.

4

5

6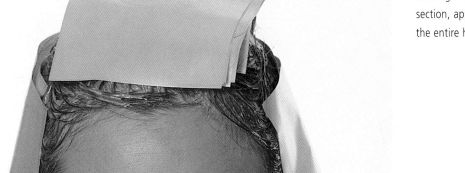

Starting at the nape and working section by section, apply the semi-permament colour to cover the entire head.

Leave under heat/Climazon for 15 minutes, then shampoo and condition as normal.

Finishing

1

Using a Denman vent brush, blow-dry the hair into a bob shape.

2

Because the hair was cut through the comb with no tension there is no graduation – just a completely sharp, beautiful, one length bob.

GRADUATED BOB (1)

Precision-cut outline with square graduation.

Cutting

Fine strawberry blonde hair losing its copper sheen with maturity.

Take your first section horizontally behind the ears, just below the occipital bone. Comb hair until the tension is completely even. Gently press the hair against the skin with either the back of your hand or your fingers and cut a straight line at the nape of the neck.

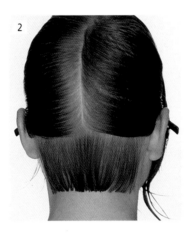

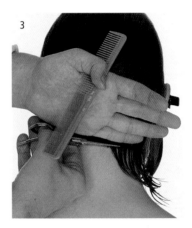

Once you have completed your guide line, continue taking sections in this fashion. Each section should be approximately 2 cm wide. As you work up above the occipital bone, your sections should become diagonal and should not go above the top of the ears. Stop when you reach the crown.

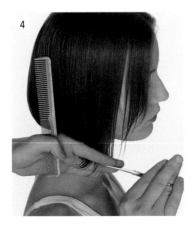

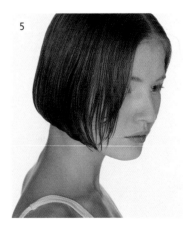

Take a section from the temple to the hair you cut in steps 1 and 2. Comb hair until the tension is even. Hold the hair gently in your fingers and cut, making sure you hold the hair as close to the skin as possible. Work up in this fashion until you reach the centre top. Then do the same on the other side.

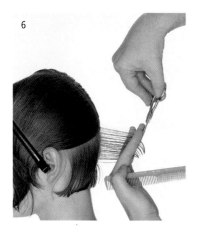

6

You are now ready to start graduating the back. Take a panel from just above the occipital bone to behind the ears, starting at the centre back. Take a vertical section approximately 1 cm wide, pull out at a 45 degree angle and cut. The hair at the nape should still be approximately 3 cm long, so there should be very little cut at the bottom. Be careful not to cut into your guide line, as this will alter the shape of your haircut. As you move across the head towards the ears, you should be pulling each section straight back. Be careful not to over direct back to your original section.

7

Continue to take horizontal panels approximately 5 cm wide. It should take you about 3 panels to work up to the crown. Continue taking vertical sections, at a 45 degree angle, pulling each section straight out from the head. Each panel should blend into the longest part of the previously cut panel. Make sure both sides are cut the same.

8

Once the back is completed, over direct all the hair in front of the ears back to the graduation you cut in step 7.

Colouring

1

Take a fine slice from the parting and place it over a Colour Wrap. Using a Colour Stroker, apply a barrier cream from the roots down to the ends.

2

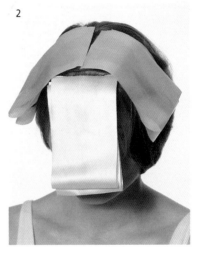

Repeat on the other side of the parting and the fringe area.

3

4

5

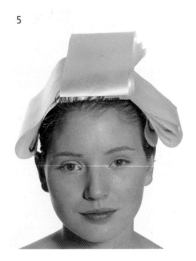

Starting at the nape, apply the semi-permanent colour using the Colour Stroker. Continue this working pattern to cover the rest of the hair.

Colour technique is now complete. Allow to develop under heat/Climazon for 15 minutes. Then rinse hair thoroughly.

PRODUCTS USED

- Wella stain guard
- Color Touch 8/43 Indian Copper mixed in equal parts with Color Touch Developer
- SP 4.V Designing Fluid
- SP 3.E Active Repair Fluid

Blow-dry the hair using a Denman classic brush for smooth finish.

Note that there are no heavy weight lines and the graduation has a beautiful bevelled shape.

CUT: COLIN GREANEY   COLOUR: MARK CREED   MAKE-UP: JENNY JORDAN   CLOTHES STYLING: CHERYL KONTEH   PHOTO: BARRY HOLLYWOOD

GRADUATED BOB (2)

Graduated bob with a round bevelled neckline.

Cutting

The model's hair was in a grown-out bob shape. She still wanted a bob but with more bounce and swing.

The model wanted the sides to be in line with her lips. Start at the side so that you can cut your line on the face to the desired length.

The line into the back will create a round neckline. Angle the line downwards into the centre back using the side panel as the guide.

5

Take your first panel from ear to ear. Take
the first section at 45 degrees, continue the
section parallel to the head and continue
this line into the next panel to the crown.

6

TIP

Take care to keep the same
tension on each section.

7

Continue into the sides over directing to
the back of the ear.

Finishing

1

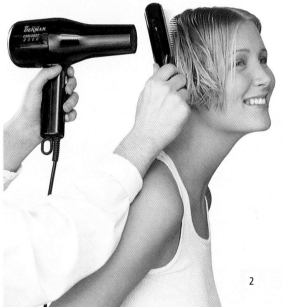

Using a Denman classic brush,
dry the hair section by section.

2

TIP

Make sure you dry the
lengths right the way through
to the ends. If you do not,
the ends will not be neat.

PRODUCTS
USED

• SP 4.V Designing Fluid

• SP 3.E Active Repair
  Fluid

CUT: COLIN GREANEY   MAKE-UP: JENNY JORDAN   CLOTHES STYLING: FRANCESCA   PHOTO: SIMON EMETT

ONE LENGTH BOB
WITH A FRINGE

Precision-cut outline complemented
by a square-cut fringe.

Colouring

The model's hair is medium fine and was heavily highlighted. The model wanted darker, warm shiny hair. The cut will have a sharp square-cut fringe and a square blunt-cut outline.

1

Apply a pre-pigmentation rinse to the whole head using a Colour Stroker. Leave to develop for 5 minutes under heat/Climazon. Rinse and dry with a hairdryer.

2

3

Take a section 2 cm under the parting and place a fine woven mesh on a Colour Wrap. Apply the colour with a Colour Stroker.

4

Finished sections. Note only the underneath layer has been coloured using the Colour Wraps.

5

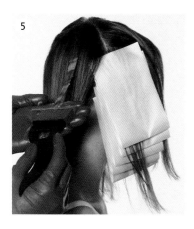

6

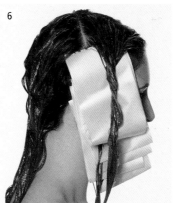

Use a Colour Stroker to apply the target shade to the middle lengths and ends, starting 4 cm from the scalp. Leave to develop for 10 minutes under heat/Climazon.

7

Mix fresh colour of the same shade and apply to root area. Develop for a further 10 minutes under heat/Climazon. When development is complete, rinse, shampoo and condition as normal.

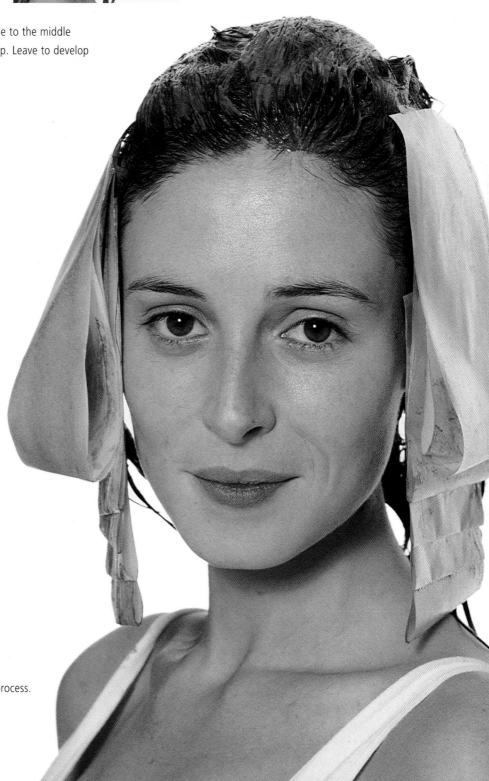

8
Colour finished. Allow to process.

Cutting

1

2

Section the hair parallel to the hairline. From the centre back, stretching the hair firmly and following the natural fall, cut a slightly inverted line. Continue this on both sides up to the crown and to the centre top of the ear.

3

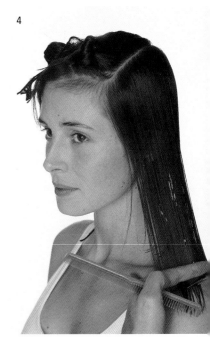

4

Follow the line through into the sides, allowing the section to relax slightly over the ear to allow for the ear lifting the outline. Continue this line on both sides up to a centre parting.

5

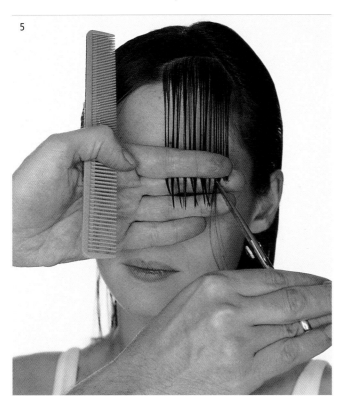

Separate a triangular section from temple to temple (the head shape determines the heaviness of the fringe). Point cutting the fringe gives a naturalistic effect. Continue this square line and point technique on each section.

6

Finishing

Apply a blow-drying lotion then start blow-drying at the fringe – this is the shortest hair and needs to be dried first, before it dries. This also allows your client to get an idea of the look.

It is important to get a very straight finish. Using a Denman classic brush, lift the hair at the root and follow down the length of the hair with the hairdryer to keep all stray ends smooth, creating finish and shine. When you get to the end of the section, reverse your brush position. This will give the required straightness to fall on the shoulder line.

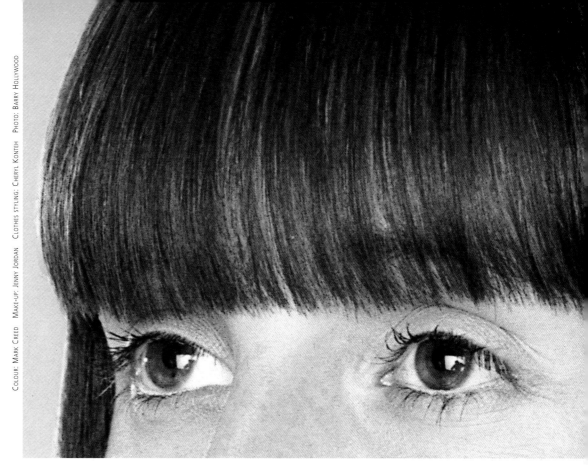

COLOUR: MARK CREED   MAKE-UP: JENNY JORDAN   CLOTHES STYLING: CHERYL KONTEH   PHOTO: BARRY HOLLYWOOD

A simple effective long bob
with superb shine and
finish, the hair gleaming
with health and beauty.

PRODUCTS
USED

- Koleston Perfect 8/43
  Celtic Copper mixed
  with 12% Welloxon
  Perfect Creme Developer

- Koleston Perfect 6/75
  Rich Heather mixed with
  12% Welloxon Perfect
  Creme Developer

- SP 4.V Designing Fluid

- SP 3.E Active Repair Fluid

CLASSIC LONG LAYERS

Long layers creating a loose natural shape.

Cutting

The model's hair was approximately the desired overall length at the back but she required more shape around the face. The outline length at the back is cut in the same way as the classic shoulder length bob (see page 42), then the outline shape is created around the face. The hair may be dressed for greater volume.

1

Starting from a centre parting, cut a line from the corner of the eye to meet the corner of the square bob-shaped back, and continue this on both sides until your sectioning reaches the crown.

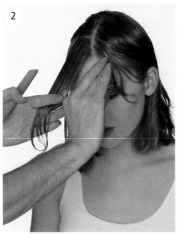

2

3

TIP

Take care that the head is in the same position and each section is held out at the same angle to the head.

4

Lifting the top sections (everything above the
temple line), layer them away to a line as
shown. This layering will give you total
versatility when dressing the hair.

5

Colouring

1

Starting at the nape of the neck, take a section 1 cm in depth and slightly narrower than the Colour Wrap. Weave out a fine section and apply the mid-tone colour.

2

Continue to a little way above the occipital bone, alternating your colours and making sure you keep the weave even.

3

Taking sections on each side of your first packets, repeat to the same level.

Return to the centre panel and continue up to the crown, making sure you end on your lightest colour at the top.

Moving to the side temple area, take your section at a 45 degree angle to the face and continue up to the ear level. From that point return the sections to the horizontal.

6

To improve the look of the hair which contained old colour, a tone on tone semi-permanent was applied between the packets and the whole head processed for 20 minutes.

Finishing

Apply mousse evenly to wet hair.

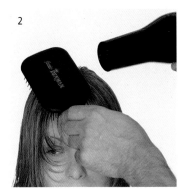

Dry the hair using a paddle brush, brushing backwards and forwards across the centre parting to create root lift.

When the hair is half dry, use a classic brush, guiding each section in the desired direction for the finished look.

Colour: Karl Forsyth-Gray   Photo: Barry Hollywood

PRODUCTS
USED

- Koleston Perfect 12/7
  Special Velvet Blonde
  mixed with 12% Welloxon
  Perfect Creme Developer

- Koleston Perfect 8/7 Velvet
  Blonde and 8/3 Light
  Golden Blonde mixed in
  equal parts with 9%
  Welloxon Perfect Creme
  Developer

- Koleston Perfect 8/3 Light
  Golden Blonde and 8/34
  Copper Golden mixed in
  equal parts with 9%
  Welloxon Perfect Creme
  Developer

- SP 4.V Designing Fluid

- SP 4.Z Finishing Spray

CLASSIC SHORT LAYERS

Short layered shape with texture
throughout the interior.

Cutting

The model's hair had been cut into a shortish layered rounded shape with no particular definition. After consultation, the model decided to have a soft textured crop.

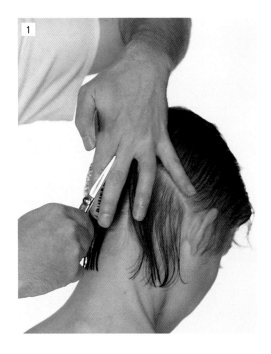

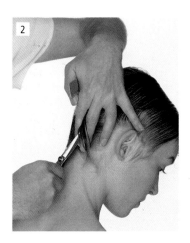

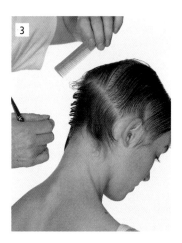

Start the cut at the centre back. Take a section underneath the occipital bone and cut vertically into the nape (approximately 2 cm long). Keeping the section parallel to the head shape, continue all the way across the back.

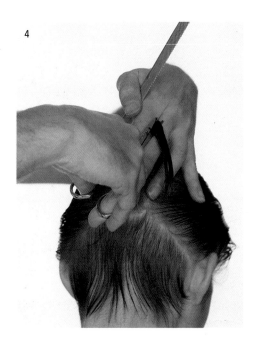

Continue your line up to the crown, keeping your line straight to your original. This creates a length of about 4 cm at the crown.

Sectioning from the temple to the back of the head, hold the hair out square to the head. Using your side section as your guide, continue into the back section and work this line parallel to the sides of the head until you reach the front hairline.

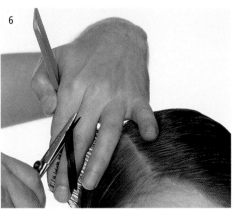

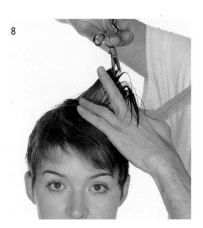

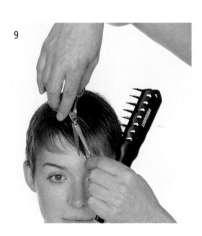

All the hair above the temple line will be cut for a texturised effect. Continue the line started in your previous panel, but on these sections cut long V-sections into the ends. Continue over the central parting from both sides.

Create the fringe length by overlay cutting, sliding in texture from the top to the desired length of the ends.

Colouring

From the crown take a fine slice of hair and place on a Colour Wrap. Using a Colour Stroker, apply the three colours to the same section of hair in bands to give the appearance of light and shadow. Continue working towards the hairline.

Finished front section.

3

4

Continue this working
pattern down the sides.

5

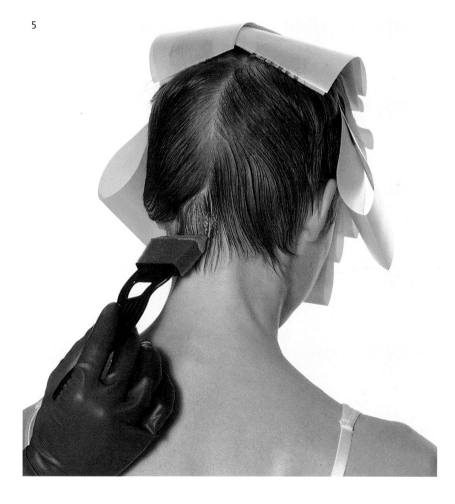

Apply the semi-permanent colour with a
Colour Stroker to the rest of the hair.

6

Leave the colour to develop for 15
minutes under heat/Climazon, then
shampoo and condition as normal.

Finishing

Using a Denman vent brush, brush the hair from side to side following gently with the hairdryer.
Finish with a light pomade. Add a light gel to create texture.

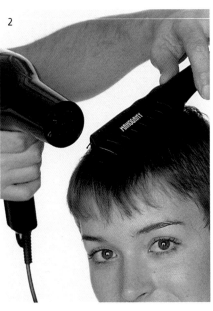

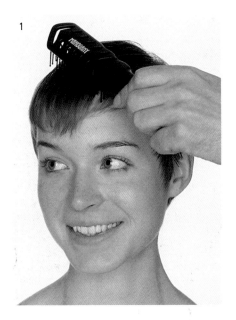

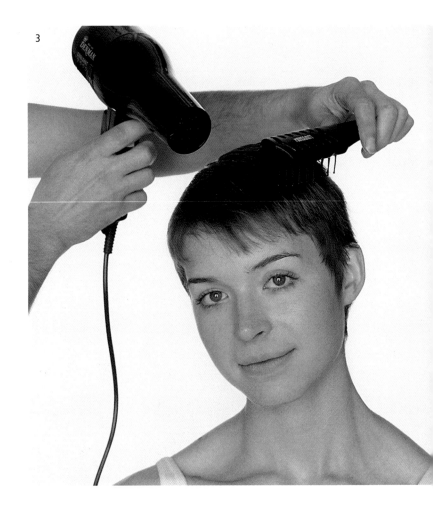

PRODUCTS USED

- Koleston Perfect 5/46 Deep Burgundy Red mixed with 9% Welloxon Perfect Creme Developer

- Koleston Perfect 9/5 Soft Oyster Beige mixed with 9% Welloxon Perfect Creme Developer

- Koleston Perfect 8/4 Sunset Red mixed with 9% Welloxon Perfect Creme Developer

- Color Touch 7/73 Sienna mixed in equal parts with Color Touch Developer

- SP 4.V Designing Fluid

- High Hair Shine Mousse Pomade

- SP 4.Y Defining Gel

CLASSIC MEN'S CUT

Classic men's tapered shape using
the natural growth pattern.

Cutting

The model's hair had grown out from his previous haircut and had become too bulky at the sides. After consultation we agreed on a shorter, sharper but still textured image.

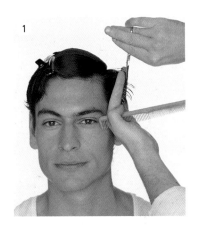

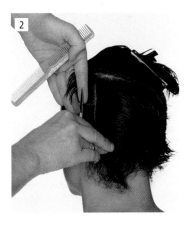

Section off the first panel from the temple to just below the crown. Take your first section at the temples and cut vertically, angling your fingers in towards the ear. The hair should be approximately 2 cm long at the top of the section and approximately 1 cm long at the bottom. Repeat on opposite side.

Continue in this fashion, but as you move round the head to behind the ears, continue the sections down to the nape area. Repeat on opposite side.

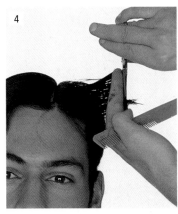

Take your next panel just below a centre parting around to the centre back, just below the crown. Continue taking vertical sections, using the previously cut hair underneath as your guide line. Start at the temple and make sure your section stays parallel to the head, as this will achieve a gradual build up of weight around the crown. Move around the head to the centre back and repeat on the other side.

6

You will now be left with the centre top panel left uncut. To achieve the desired textured look, take horizontal sections across the top of the head. Starting at the crown, cut into the hair at different lengths. Take care not to cut the hair too short as this will make the rest of the haircut appear unbalanced. Continue in this manner towards the front of the head.

7

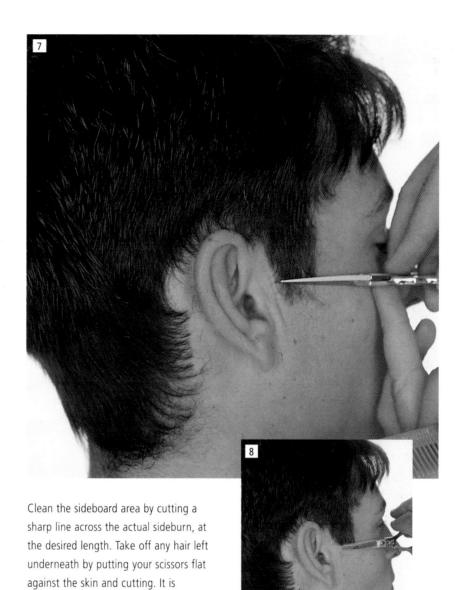

8

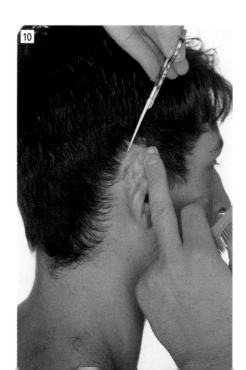

Clean the sideboard area by cutting a sharp line across the actual sideburn, at the desired length. Take off any hair left underneath by putting your scissors flat against the skin and cutting. It is important to keep the movement of your scissors as flowing as possible.

9

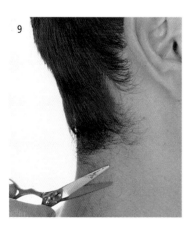

Use the same technique to take off fuzzy hair at the nape.

10

Take off any untidy hair around the ears by gently pulling the ear down and cutting a sharp line.

Finishing

1

Blow-dry using a Denman vent brush to achieve texture.

2

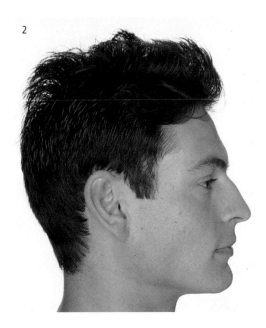

You should have no weight lines anywhere in the haircut, and it should hug the natural shape of the head.

CUT: COLIN GREANEY   PHOTO: BARRY HOLLYWOOD

PRODUCTS USED

- SP 3.S Restructuring Complex with Liquid Hair
- High Hair Shine Mousse Pomade

PART 3: ADVANCED LOOKS

Make a good haircut into to a great haircut.

Collections gallery

CRUSH 97   GREY ZISSER

CRUSH 97   GREY ZISSER

CUE 96   GREY ZISSER

CUE 96   GREY ZISSER

PRISM 96   GREY ZISSER

PRISM 96   GREY ZISSER

GARÇON 95   AKOS

GARÇON 95   AKOS

TRIBERAMA 94   AKOS

TRIBERAMA 94

CRUSH 97   GREY ZISSER

CRUSH 97   GREY ZISSER

CUE 96   GREY ZISSER

CUE 96   GREY ZISSER

PRISM 96   GREY ZISSER

PRISM 96   GREY ZISSER

GARÇON 95   AKOS

GARÇON 95   AKOS

TRIBERAMA 94   AKOS

TRIBERAMA 94   AKOS

TECHNIQUE 93   AKOS

TECHNIQUE 93   AKOS

ORB 93   AKOS

ORB 93   AKOS

DASH 92   JOEL O'SULLIVAN

DASH 92   JOEL O'SULLIVAN

WHITE HOT 92   JOEL O'SULLIVAN

WHITE HOT 92   JOEL O'SULLIVAN

MEN 91   TESSA & VIKKI

MEN 91   TESSA & VIKKI

TECHNIQUE 93 AKOS

TECHNIQUE 93 AKOS

ORB 93 AKOS

ORB 93 AKOS

DASH 92 JOEL O'SULLIVAN

DASH 92 JOEL O'SULLIVAN

WHITE HOT 92 JOEL O'SULLIVAN

WHITE HOT 92 JOEL O'SULLIVAN

MEN 91 TESSA & VIKKI

MEN 91 TESSA & VIKKI

Fringes

Long and sleek or short and choppy fringes have Fringe Benefits.

ROUNDED GRADUATION

Head-hugging graduation following the
natural contours of the head.

Cutting

The model wanted more shape and a funkier look.

1

2

3

Take a centre parting from the crown to the nape. Take a section parallel to the head and angle your line upwards towards the cheekbones. Continue to the crown and then connect in the side sections, working up to the centre parting. Do the same on the other side.

4

5

Start your graduation parallel to the head directly above the centre of the ear. Continue the line forward to the front hairline. Then work from your starting point to the centre back. Use the same technique on the opposite side.

6

7

Continue the line into the top sections, working both sides across the centre parting. Then texturise the front by holding 1 cm-square sections and gently skim off the top layer using overlay cutting technique.

8

Colouring

1

Section hair into two zones from the temples to the occipital bone. Using a downward movement from roots to ends, apply your first colour to the under sections with a Colour Stroker.

2

3

Separate the two zones by covering the under sections with Colour Wraps. Colour the top zone with your second colour. Allow to process for 20 minutes.

4

5

6

7

COLOUR: MARK CREED   MAKE-UP: JENNY JORDAN   CLOTHES STYLIST: CHERYL KONTEH   PHOTO: PAUL BURLEY

Finishing

Blow-dry the hair and dress with pomade.

PRODUCTS USED

- Color Touch 5/5 Alizarin and 0/56 Purple Fire mixed in equal parts with Color Touch Developer

- Color Touch 6/4 Venetian Red and 0/46 Red Fire mixed in equal parts with Color Touch Developer

- SP 4.Y Defining Gel

- High Hair Shine Mousse Pomade

FREEHAND MEN'S CUT

Modern men's cut that can be worn

forward or quiffed back.

Cutting

Our model is in a band and wanted a glam Chelsea boy look, but the hair lay flat. There are no sharp lines in this haircut and it should be variable and textured.

1

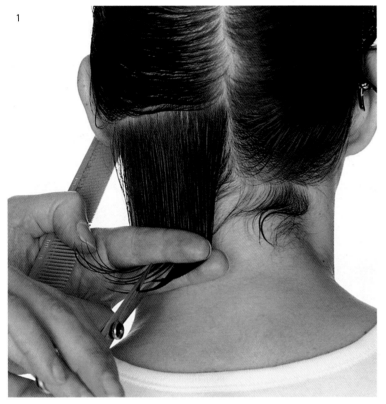

Start with a centre back parting and, taking horizontal sections up to the occipital bone, cut long V-shapes into each section. The shorter hair at the point of each V and the longer hair at the sides of each V should be the same length throughout the cut. This will create a perfect balance within the shape as the cut grows out.

2

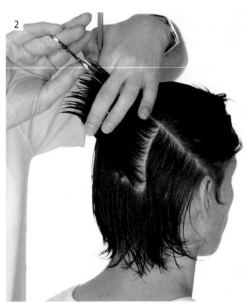

3

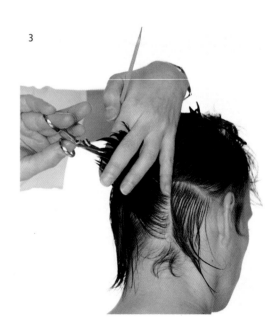

Above the occipital bone change to vertical sections. This will give the overall cut a lighter, airier feel.

Start the sides at the front, holding the sections slightly forward. Blend these desired lengths into your back panel lengths.

Continue your sections up in to the top panel of the head, cross-checking over the centre parting and creating the fringe length so that the hair can be worn forward or quiffed away.

Colouring

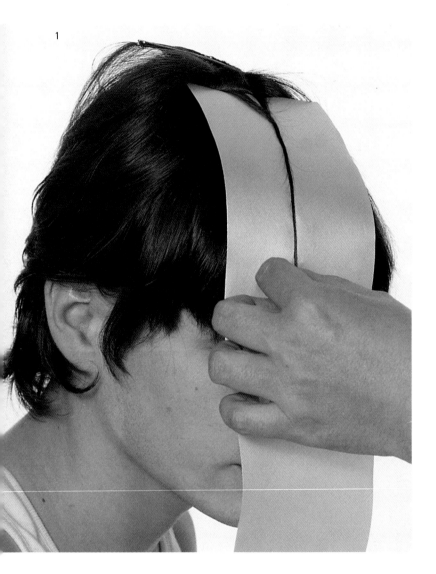

1

At the crown take a section in the fingers and twist lightly.
Place on the Colour Wrap.

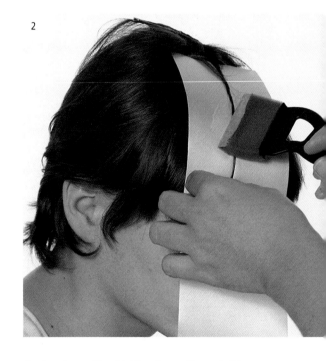

2

Apply colour without letting the section untwist.

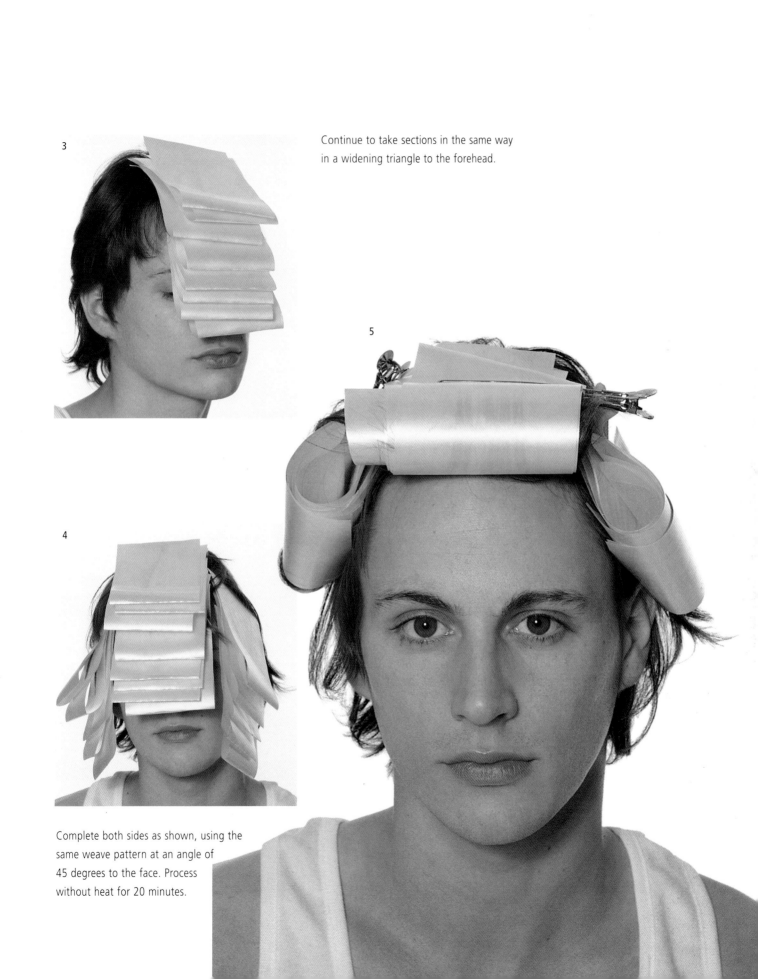

3

Continue to take sections in the same way in a widening triangle to the forehead.

5

4

Complete both sides as shown, using the same weave pattern at an angle of 45 degrees to the face. Process without heat for 20 minutes.

Finishing

1

Apply gel evenly to wet hair. Using your fingers like a claw, lift the hair up and away creating lots of root lift during the drying.

2

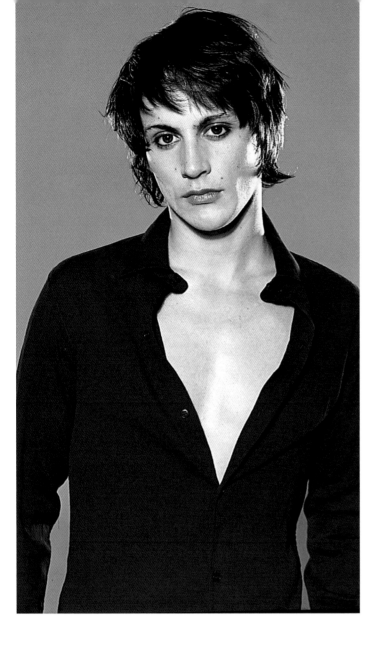

COLOUR: KARL FORSYTH-GRAY   PHOTO: BARRY HOLLYWOOD

PRODUCTS USED

- Koleston Perfect 6/3 Dark Golden Blonde mixed with 6% Welloxon Perfect Creme Developer

- Koleston Perfect 8/73 Golden Sand mixed with 9% Welloxon Perfect Creme Developer

- Color Touch 6/7 Persimmon mixed in equal parts with Color Touch Developer

- SP 4.Y Defining Gel

- SP 4.Z Finishing Spray

TEXTURED HORIZONTAL
SECTIONING TECHNIQUE

Freefall soft geometric look.

Colouring

The model's hair had been cut into a short bob shape but she wanted a look which would still be worn smooth but with a looser textured feel and golden sunny colour.

1

Take approximately 12 Colour Wraps at a time and prefold them. This will make it easier to fold them with precision when they are placed in the hair.

2

Weave a band 1 cm back from the hairline followed by four individual highlights into the first section.

TIP

Seal the folded Colour Wrap by pressing it with your comb.

3

4

For the next section, take only a band. Place in Colour Wrap as for previous section.

Repeat steps 1–3 on the opposite side.

5

6

7

Cutting

1

Start the cut on the side. Lift the first section at 45 degrees to the side of the head and cut short triangular lines into the edge. Continue this technique up to the centre.

2

3

4

5

The outline is cleaned up still using the same technique.

Using the original line as a guide, continue graduating the hair into the nape.

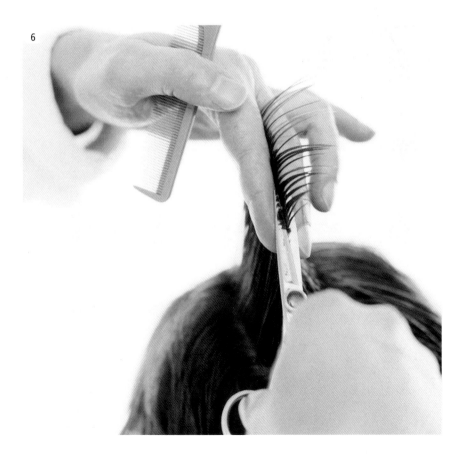

6

As you get to the back of the head, lift the hair to 90 degrees to keep it parallel with the head.

7

Follow the same technique on the opposite side.

8

9

Connect the line across the top and then cut V-shapes into the lengths to create your texture.

The finished cut and colour before drying.

PRODUCTS
USED

- Koleston Perfect 10/3
  Light Golden Blonde
  mixed with 12%
  Welloxon Perfect
  Creme Developer

- SP 3.S Restructuring
  Complex with Liquid
  Hair

- High Hair Shine
  Mousse Pomade

- SP 4.Z Finishing Spray

COLOUR: MARK CREED   PHOTO: GREY ZISSER

ASYMMETRIC CUT

Controlled asymmetric shape.

Cutting

The model's hair was in a grown-out short graduated bob. She wanted something shorter and more geometric.

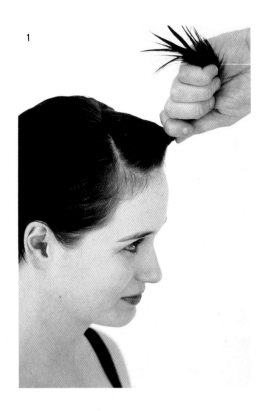

1

2

Section off a centre triangle and pin away. Then, starting with a vertical section directly over the ear, work your sections forward to the front hairline, over directing the hair back to your first section.

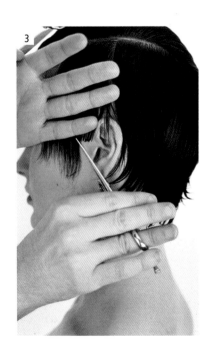

3

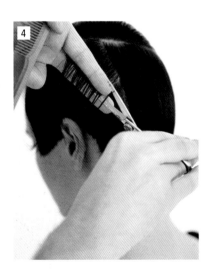

4

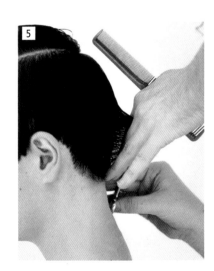

5

Cut the outline shape on the skin and then connect in the back hair using your first section as your guide to create a round graduated back. Continue this technique into opposite side.

Connect in the top sections, over directing the front from left to right to create the asymmetry. Cut the outline shape of the fringe created by over directing from left to right.

Colouring

On the shorter side, take three 2 cm-wide sections to lay on top of each other.

Continue the technique on the longer side of the front section, then apply your overall full head colour through the remaining hair. Allow to process for 20 minutes, following manufacturer's instructions.

Blow-dry and dress the hair.

PRODUCTS USED

- Koleston Perfect 12/03 Special Beige Blonde (in Colour Wraps)

- Koleston Perfect 6/3 Dark Golden Blonde and 5/4 Deep Autumn Chestnut mixed in equal parts with 6% Welloxon Perfect Creme Developer (full head colour)

- SP 1.8 Colour Vitalising Cleanser

- SP 3.8 Colour Saver

CUT: COLIN GREANEY   COLOUR: KARL FORSYTH-GRAY   CLOTHES STYLING: CHERYL KONTEH   PHOTO: GREY ZISSER

FEATHERING TECHNIQUE

Heavy square-cut fringe working into
long feathered layers.

Cutting

The model wanted a very feathery effect, with length but some definition, and a navy black sheen. After consultation, we opted for a heavily cut-into shape with a hard solid fringe, and we decided to pre-lift a segment shape through the fringe before colouring the rest of the head.

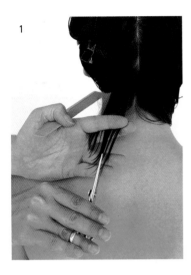

Start at the back and keep the length but cut into each section to a depth of 5–6 cm using the V-shape technique. Each section must be controlled to maintain a balance through the shape.

Continue with the technique through the back of the head up to the crown.

5

The feathery texture at the back of the head is now finished.

6

Comb the hair onto the face – the hair should be very wet. Cut a C-shape around the cheek bones to meet the outline. Continue this line on both sides and join the fringe across the centre.

7

Hold the fringe hair as close to the face as possible so as not to create graduation.

8

9

Using the back as your guide line, continue the texture through the top of the hair.

Colouring

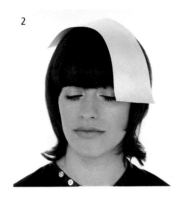

TIP

The barrier cream prevents the colour running.

Dry the hair into the finished look. Paint a barrier cream onto the entire side of a Colour Wrap and place it on the head.

Repeat the process on another Colour Wrap and apply it to the hair. Press to seal both Colour Wraps.

Cover the bleach with another Colour Wrap so that it does not dry out. Allow to process to an orange colour before rinsing the bleach from the hair. Apply a full head colour mixed with intensive developer. Allow to process for 20 minutes, then rinse and condition.

Apply bleach with 12% peroxide to the exposed hair.

Blow-dry the fringe area smooth with a Denman classic brush and finger-dry the back for texture.

PRODUCTS USED

- Blondor Special mixed with 12% Welloxon Perfect Creme Developer

- Color Touch 2/88 Blue Moon mixed with Color Touch Intensive Developer (main colour)

- SP 3.S Restructuring Complex with Liquid Hair

- High Hair Shine Mousse Pomade

THE DASH

Undercut shape where the underneath section
is visually checked in to the top.

Cutting

The model's hair had previously been cut into a one length bob, which can drag down fine features. After consultation, the model accepted our advice and decided to go for a shorter, graduated, layered bob, with the underneath sections disconnected.

1

Take a triangular panel from the crown to the temples and clip it out of the way securely – you will not be cutting this until later on.

2

Start the haircut at the centre back, taking a section above the occipital bone. Cut vertically into the nape (approximately 3 cm long), keeping the section parallel to the head shape, and continue all the way across the back.

3

Take the next panel just below the crown to behind the ears. Working with vertical sections, continue the haircut by following on from your previous panel and work across the back of the head in this fashion. This will achieve a gradual build up of weight above the occipital bone.

4

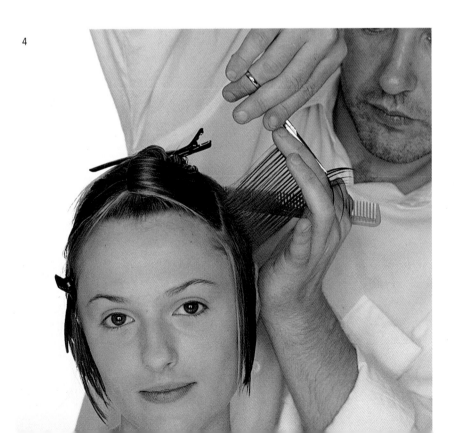

Your next panels are the sides. Take a vertical section above the ear and pull out at a 45 degree angle. As you cut this section, ensure the angle of your fingers will leave the hair shorter at the top part of the section. This gives a soft, layered effect. Continue towards the temple, but as you move in front of the ear over direct each section to the original guide line. Repeat on the opposite side.

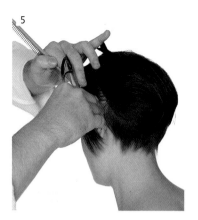

5

6

7

One you have completed the side panels in front of the ears, you will need to check in the hair behind the ears. Take a vertical section and, working from your previous guide line, continue to blend into the hair you cut in step 3. Work round the head on each side to the centre back.

Unclip the hair from step 1. Section off a panel from 1 cm behind the temples. Cut the first section from the centre of the top of the head, over directing back to the longest point of the hair you cut in step 6. Continue across the head until you run out of hair.

8

9

Section off your next panel using a side parting. Begin to layer the heaviest side of the parting, working from the interior part of the haircut to the exterior part, remembering that the exterior part of the haircut will be disconnected and over hang from the previously cut side panels of the hair. The first section you take should be above the ear. Over direct each section back to this point. As you get towards the front part of the head (around the temples), begin to point cut the hair. When completed, section a side parting on the opposite side of the head and repeat the same technique. There will be very little hair to cut on this side.

TIP

Point cutting will give more extreme lengths.

Colouring

At the crown at an angle of
60 degrees to the parting take a
slice section 5 cm wide, place on a
Colour Wrap and apply the lightest
colour. Repeat on two more sections
leaving no space in between.

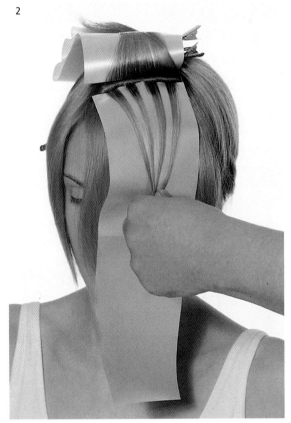

Now widen the section to the width of a Colour
Wrap and, using a chunky weave, alternate between
the chosen colours.

Continue until you are 3 cm from the
front hairline, ending the weaving
with a finer section of your mid-tone
colour.

4

Alternate your sections between chunks of your lightest colour and slices of your other colours, with the last section being a mid-tone.

5

Moving to the other side, take a section parallel to the parting and set back 3 cm from the parting. Using a chunky weave, apply your lightest colour.

6

Apply a tone on tone colour to the rest of the hair, including the hair between the packets of colour. Process for 25 minutes.

Finishing

1

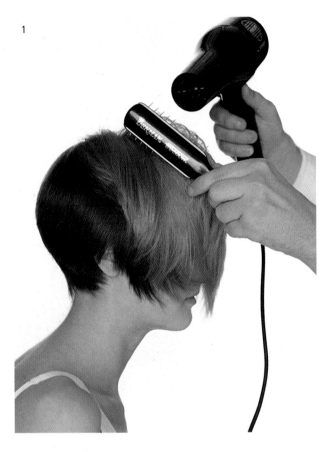

Blow-dry using a Denman vent brush, to give a smooth polished look.

2

Notice how the disconnected hair through the sides and top appears visually to be checked in, but technically is not. The object of this haircut is to have a shattered outline, with no heavy weight lines. It can be worn pushed to any side, tucked behind the ears... In fact, it's a very versatile haircut!

Cut: Colin Greaney Colour: Karl Forsyth-Gray Photo: Barry Hollywood

PRODUCTS
USED

Highlights:

• Koleston Perfect 9/7 Soft
  Velvet Blonde mixed with
  12% Welloxon Perfect
  Creme Developer

• Koleston Perfect 10/0
  Lightest Blonde mixed
  with 9% Welloxon
  Perfect Creme Developer

• Koleston Perfect 8/3
  Light Golden Blonde and
  8/43 Claret Copper
  mixed with 6% Welloxon
  Perfect Creme Developer

Colour pack:

• Color Touch 8/0 Natural
  Light Blonde mixed in
  equal parts with Color
  Touch Developer

• Colour Touch 7/7 Warm
  Amber mixed in equal
  parts with Color Touch
  Developer

• Color Touch 8/33 Indian
  Gold mixed in equal
  parts with Color Touch
  Developer

• SP 4.V Designing Fluid

• SP 3.E Active Repair Fluid

THE CRUSH

Freehand cut with graduation and layering.

Cutting

Our model wanted a more gamine look that would update her commercial flip style. Her hair had previously been coloured and had very fine copper-gold highlights.

Section out the fringe from temple to temple allowing the hair to follow its natural hair growth pattern and cut a straight fringe from temple to temple.

Connect opposite side of the fringe.

Begin the side by taking a section parallel to the hair-line. Lift the hair at 45 degrees and cut an angle following on from the fringe line.

Continue to lift the hair at 45 degrees as you cut into the nape and up to the centre parting.

5

Side finished.

6

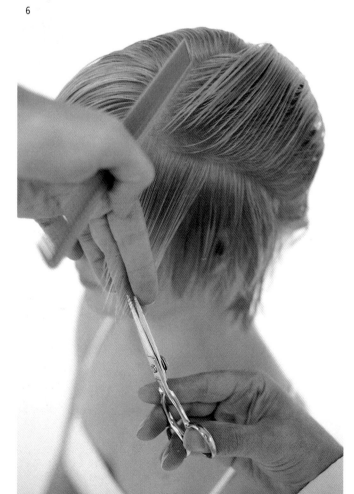

Cut the opposite side
in the same way.

Continue line into the nape.

Taking horizontal sections and lifting at 45 degrees, cut a concave line into the nape hair. This creates flatness through the centre and leaves weight behind the ear.

Continue this line up to 1 cm above the occipital bone.

Section a panel across the back of the head, then, taking vertical sections, continue the line, keeping all your sections parallel to the head.

Section another panel across the crown and continue the line.

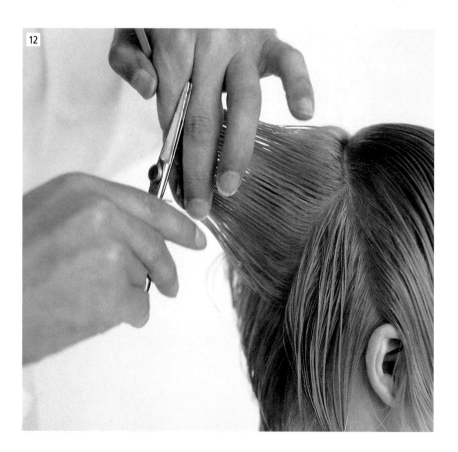

The last section is directed back to produce a square line across the back.

Continue your line into the top of the hair. This angle will leave length through to top front.

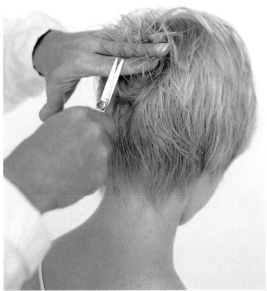

Slide your fingers across the scalp and twist through 90 degrees. This action twists the section. Slice into the remaining hair with your scissors.

15

Continue this technique over the entire head.

16

Slice away a third of the hair between your fingers.

17

Overlay cut the fringe to produce a distressed texture. The cut is now finished.

TIPS

● The Crush will suit most face shapes as the outline layering and graduation can be customised to suit the individual.

● Overlay cutting skims off the top layer without removing the outside edge.

Colouring

Having made two diagonal partings to form a triangle from the natural crown to the hairline, take your first section to be coloured.

On the right side, take a slice 6 cm below the parting, approximately 4 cm wide and 1 cm deep, and apply colour using a Colour Wrap.

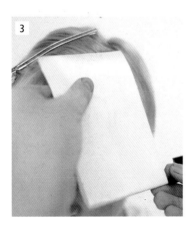

Take a slice 2 cm above the last section and repeat procedure. Then take a slice 6 cm wide at a new parting and apply colour to the section.

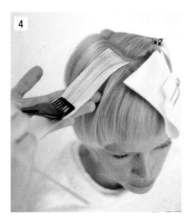

Move to the left-hand side 4 cm below the parting. Take a 6 cm slice and apply the colour. Repeat the process in another slice at the parting but reducing the width of this slice to 3 cm.

Leave to process for 20 minutes under heat/Climazon, then shampoo.

COLOUR: KARL FORSYTH-GRAY   MAKE-UP: HONEY TWIGGS   CLOTHES STYLING: CHERYL KONTEH   PHOTO: GREY ZISSER

Finishing

Blow-dry the hair with your fingers. Texture and weight distribution are integral to the finish.

PRODUCTS USED

- Koleston Perfect 9/7 Soft Velvet Blonde mixed with 9% Welloxon Perfect Creme Developer

- Koleston Perfect 8/34 Copper Gold mixed with 9% Welloxon Perfect Creme Developer

- SP 4.Y Defining Gel

- High Hair Shine Mousse Pomade

TEXTURED PAGEBOY

The new pageboy shape with a
very modern finish.

Cutting

The model had mid-length medium-textured blonde highlighted hair. She wanted a stronger sexier look that would still have versatility.

1

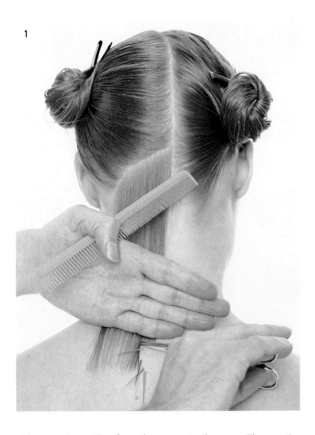

2

Take a centre parting from the crown to the nape. Then section parallel to the hair-line, cutting a line angled towards the jaw. Continue up to the crown.

3

Connect the side sections into the back and work your sections up to the centre parting. Continue into the opposite side using the same technique.

4

5

6

To create a long tapered fringe, cut long V-sections into the ends. Then continue a line into the side sections.

7

8

Continue your line to meet the corner, level with the front of the ear. Repeat on the opposite side.

Colouring

1

2

3

Weave out classic highlights and place them on top of the Colour Wrap.
Apply the colour with a Colour Stroker. Work through all your front sections
with this technique.

4

5

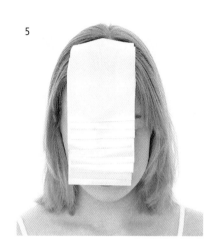

6

Continue through the whole head using a classic highlighting technique.

7

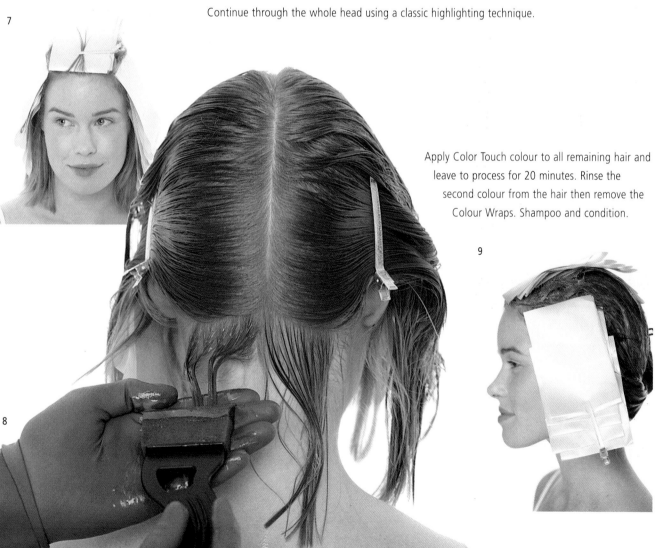

Apply Color Touch colour to all remaining hair and
leave to process for 20 minutes. Rinse the
second colour from the hair then remove the
Colour Wraps. Shampoo and condition.

9

8

Finishing

COLOUR: MARK CREED   MAKE-UP: JENNY JORDAN   PHOTO: PAUL BURLEY

Blow-dry and dress the hair.

PRODUCTS USED

- Koleston Perfect 10/3 Lightest Golden Blonde with 12% Welloxon Perfect Creme Developer

- Color Touch 9/33 Savannah Gold mixed in equal parts with Color Touch Developer

- SP 4.V Designing Fluid

- High Hair Shine Mousse Pomade

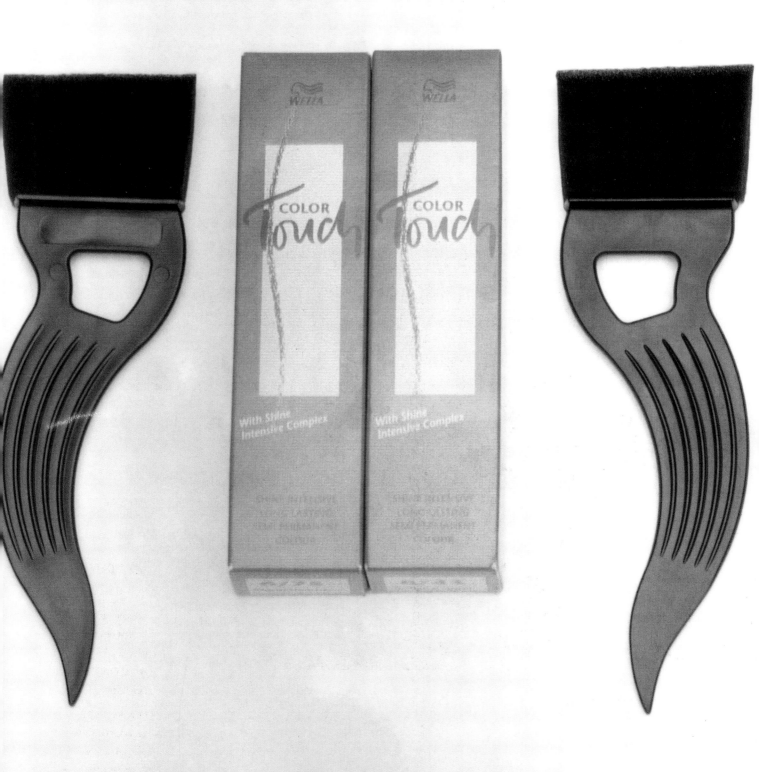

PART 4: PRODUCTS

The products you need to create the look.

Part of the artistic progress at Mahogany has been to devise and design innovative working tools that will enable us to remain on the cutting edge, to be technically flexible and to expand our creative hair fashion ideas. These simple but effective technical accessories have been successfully developed and marketed world-wide, enabling all hairdressers around the globe to share in the Mahogany energy and enthusiasm for modern hair design.

AVAILABLE IN 3 SIZES

ROVALER PERM RODS

The unique oval perm rod designed to create a close-to-real wave, ideal for creating the required movement for modern-day styles and essential for the client who wants her hair to have an undeliberate tossed fullness.

Why Rovaler perm rods?

1 Natural free-falling S-shaped curl. Softness and firmness in one rod.

2 No new training needed – if you can wind a perm, you can wind with Rovaler perm rods.

3 Can be mixed with conventional perm rods if firmer results are required.

4 Long-term tool – not a short-term gimmick. Every salon can use them to inspire their clients for new looks.

5 Can be used in any wind technique, giving clients the desired natural look without having to wait for the perm to settle.

COLOUR WRAPS

An alternative to the more harsh and uneconomical metal foil, for highlighting, lowlighting and colouring sections. These pre-packed strips are made of thin, light, styrene material. They are lighter to store, comfortable for the client and easy for the technician to use – only one fold is needed to hold them in place when applying colour. (See the step-by-step illustrations.)

Why Colour Wraps?

1 25% lighter than most foils, therefore more comfortable for the client.

2 Available in two colours so you can identify individual colours in the hair.

3 Their insulating properties retain warmth so they can process faster without necessarily using additional heat.

4 No folding is required at any of the edges, unlike foil, as the moisture of the colour adheres to the Colour Wrap.

5 No disagreeable discomfort or noise, which are common problems associated with foil.

COLOUR STROKER

An ingenious alternative to the outdated standard tinting brush. This multifaceted hair colouring tool can be used with any hair colouring products. It has a unique ergonomic handle, and the detachable foam tips, which come in two different sizes, are soft and sensitive to the client's head. The Stroker is a quick and very efficient tool when applying tint, bleach or colour conditioner.

The Stroker can also be handy when applying hair conditioning treatments.

Why Colour Stroker?

1 Ergonomic design makes it easy and comfortable to hold and use.

2 The foam tip allows colour to be absorbed and act as a colour wall, eliminating the need to load a brush.

3 Dual action handle specially designed for easy sectioning.

4 Pack comes with four interchangeable tips of two different sizes for specific jobs.

5 Spare packs of four tips available.

6 Can be used for highlighting, partial application or full-head technique.

7 Foam tips are unaffected by colour chemicals.

8 Quick, easy application of colour due to the unique stroking action.

9 Colour is easily rinsed from the pad once the handle has been removed.

10 Feels gentle and comfortable on the scalp.

BRUSHES

The classic brush

The Mahogany range of classic brushes are specially made by the highly recommended company Denman. They are available in three sizes: handbag, medium and large. They have smooth round-ended nylon pins set into a natural rubber cushion. The close-set pin formation provides exceptional grip and control, making these brushes ideal for smoothing, shaping and polishing hair.

The vent brush

The Mahogany vent brush is specially designed by Denman. This revolutionary brush incorporates a wide-spaced pin formation separated by a series of chevron vents and has a hollow brush head. This design increases the air flow to the hair, providing movement and root lift for softer, fuller hair. It is available in two sizes.

THE HAIRDRYER

The Mahogany hairdryer is specially designed by Denman to give just the right amount of power and the right number of nozzle sizes for controlled directional drying. This British-made dryer is built of the finest materials and components. It comes with a fitted plug and a detachable concentrator and is fully guaranteed for twelve months.

WELLA PRODUCTS

HAIR COLOUR

Koleston Perfect

The world's best-selling permanent hair colour. With 84 shades, Koleston Perfect has a unique synergy system to guarantee high-performance, long-lasting colour results with incredible shine.

Color Touch

A long-lasting, oxidative semi-permanent colour in 34 shades with new Shine Intensive Complex – award-winning Liquid Hair and Natural Beeswax – to strengthen and condition the hair. Ideal as an introduction to colour for colour-shy clients, or for covering those initial signs of grey.

Color Fresh

A new liquid semi-permanent colour with 15 gorgeous shades which last up to 8 washes. Containing a special Revitalising Complex to condition the hair, Color Fresh is perfect as an in-between colour refresher, leaving the hair shining with health.

Blondor Special

A high lift, blue powder bleach for natural or coloured hair. Perfect for partial or full-head colouring techniques.

SYSTEM PROFESSIONAL

3.R Liquid Hair

Containing hydrolysed keratin – the protein found in real hair – this product works from within to restructure and strengthen, leaving the hair stronger and with more volume.

3.E Active Repair Fluid

A leave-in conditioner for the lengths and ends of the hair. It contains innovative components which form a thin, protective film around damaged ends of the hair, giving lasting protection from advanced splitting.

4.V Designing Fluid

A strong hold lotion for sculpting and setting. With special moisture factors to give shine and flexibility and UV filters to protect against the harmful effects of the sun.

4.Y Defining Gel

A versatile gel for styling and finishing, it gives the hair superb long-lasting shine with a natural hold.

3.S Restructuring Complex with Liquid Hair

A leave-in mousse conditioner with natural hold to revitalise, condition and protect damaged or fine hair.

3.8 Colour Saver

An in-salon treatment to maintain the brilliance of freshly coloured hair. Colour stabilisers neutralise any oxidation residues and prolong the life of the colour whilst herbal extracts soothe the scalp and add shine.

HIGH HAIR

Shine Mousse Pomade – Pure Shine

1 Light mousse dressing for an incredible gloss finish

2 Creates shine

3 Pro-vitamin B5 for healthy hair

4 UV Screen for protection

5 Unique liquid formula dispenses as a mousse for easy application

6 Ideal for finer hair – no heaviness

Finishing Spray – Firm Control

1 Precise spraying action perfect for creating root lift

2 Shine enhancers give ultimate finishing touch

3 Excellent finishing hold to your style

4 Pro-vitamin B5 for healthy hair

5 UV Screen for protection

Wella Great Britain, Wella Road, Basingstoke, RG22 4AF, UK.
Tel: 01256 320202 Fax: 01256 471518

GLOSSARY

BANDING

When a band of colour is placed on the head to appear as a vertical stripe.

COLOUR/PERM TECHNICIAN

A hairdressing specialist. An expert who has full knowledge, technical and artistic ability and is responsible for the colour/perm department.

CONSULTATION

Initial period with client to listen, advise, direct and explain styling, colouring, perming and conditioning. (See pp. 6–7.)

GRADUATION

When the under hair is shorter than the top lengths, i.e. cut at less than a 90 degree angle to the side or back of the head.

HAIR AND SCALP MASSAGE

See 'Protein treatment' below.

HIGHLIGHTING

Weaving in of colour that is then placed either in Colour Wraps or foil. The colour is lifted lighter than the base colour.

LAYERING

When all the hair is cut to the same length at 90 degrees to the head shape. The internal lengths may be shorter than the external lengths, i.e. cut at more than 90 degrees to the sides or back.

LOWLIGHTING

Weaving in of colour that is then placed either in Colour Wraps or foil. The colour added is richer or deeper than the base colour.

ONE LENGTH

When the outline is one line. All the hair following from a parting to the outside length forms one line.

OVER DIRECT

To hold subsequent sections to the first section so that they are no longer at 90 degrees to the head, thereby building more length through these sections. This can be done forwards or backwards.

OVERLAY CUTTING

To cut by sliding your scissors over the hair in a tapering movement rather than cutting a sharp blunt edge.

PADDLE BRUSH

Flat-backed hairbrush with a 5" x 4" bristle area, ideal for smoothing hair and creating a flat shiny finish.

PANEL

A large section of the head, e.g. ear to ear below the occipital bone.

POINT CUTTING

To serrate the ends of the hair by cutting fine, sharp V-sections.

PROTEIN TREATMENT

Applying the highest quality conditioning products, giving therapeutic head massage, relaxing the client during treatment, enhancing the feel-good factor. The result is a healthy scalp and beautiful shining hair.

ROUNDED GRADUATION

To work the lengths around the shape of the head, not forming any square corners.

SECTION

A width of hair taken from a panel, approximately 1 cm wide.

SEGMENTING

When a specific shape of colour – elliptical or triangular – is placed into the hair.

SLICING

When you colour the whole section taken before you weave for highlights or lowlights.

SLIDE CUTTING

To allow the scissor blades to cut the hair by sliding down the lengths of the hair.

SQUARE GRADUATION

To maintain a square line held at just below 90 degrees to the head shape.

TAPERING

To cut a fine line into the head shape.

UNDERWRAP

To mix colour on the hair itself.

V-SECTION CUTTING

To cut long narrow V-shapes into the lengths of each section of hair.